CLIFF RICHARD

HIS GREATEST HITS

PIANO VOCAL GUITAR

Published 2001

Editor: Anna Joyce
Folio Design: Dominic Brookman

International
MUSIC
Publications

BACHELOR BOY

Words and Music by
BRUCE WELCH AND CLIFF RICHARD

1. When I was young—— my fa - ther said "Son I have
2. When I was six - teen I fell—— in love with a girl—— as

some - thing to say."—— And what he told me I'll
sweet as can be.—— But I re - mem - bered

CAN'T KEEP THIS FEELING IN

Words and Music by
ARNOLD ROMAN, STEVE SKINNER
and DENNIS LAMBERT

CARRIE

Words and Music by
TERRY BRITTEN and B.A. ROBERTSON

DO YOU WANNA DANCE

Words and Music by
ROBERT FREEMAN

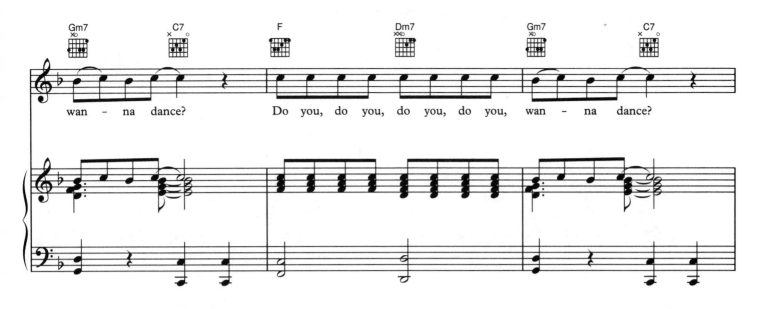

wan - na dance? Do you, do you, do you, do you, wan - na dance?

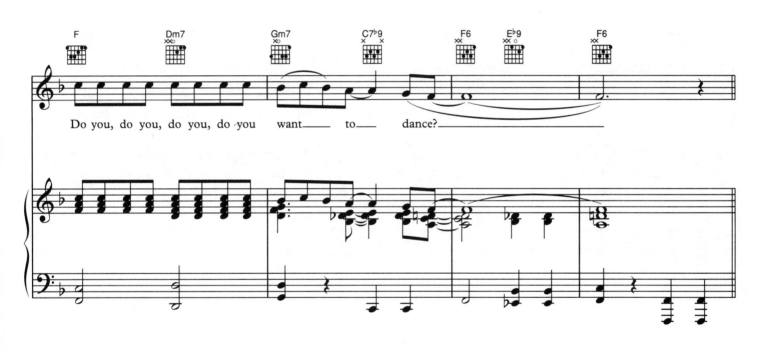

Do you, do you, do you, do you want___ to___ dance?_____

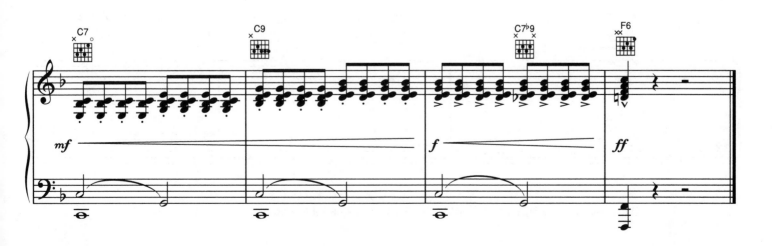

DADDY'S HOME

Words and Music by
JAMES SHEPPARD
and WILLIAM MILLER

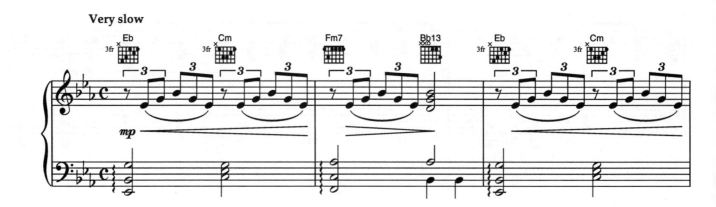

You're my love,___ you're my an - gel,___ you're the girl___ of my dreams.

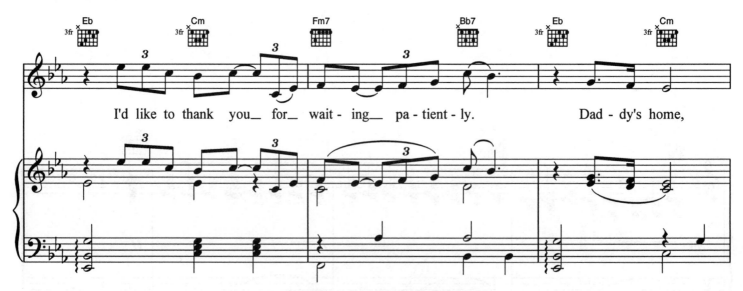

I'd like to thank you___ for___ wait - ing___ pa - tient - ly.   Dad - dy's home,

stay._____ It was-n't on a

Sun-day, Mon-day and Tues-day went by. It was-n't__ on a Tues-day__ af-ter-noon. All I could do__was cry,

but I made a prom-ise__that you trea - sure, I made it all back to you. How I

DEVIL WOMAN

Words and Music by
TERRY BRITTEN
and CHRISTINE HOLMES

I've had no-thing but bad___ luck Since the day I saw the cat at my door.___
Give me the ring on your fin - ger. Let me see the lines of your hand.___

So I came here to you,___ sweet la - dy,
I can see me a tall___ dark stran - ger

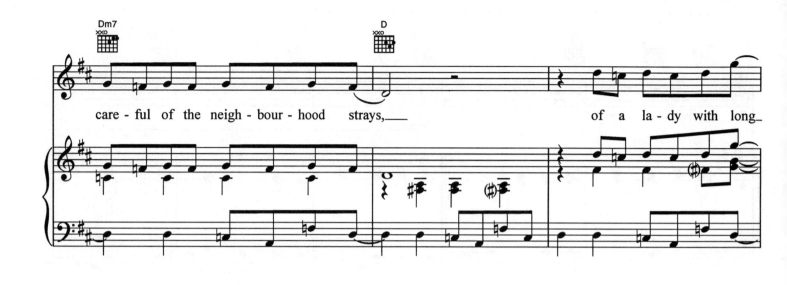

care - ful of the neigh - bour - hood strays,___ of a la - dy with long___

___ black hair___ try - in' to win you with her fem - i - nine ways.___

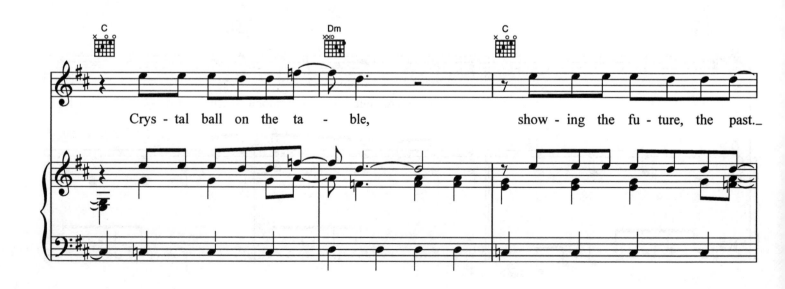

Crys - tal ball on the ta - ble, show - ing the fu - ture, the past.___

Same cat with them ev - il eyes.__ You'd

bet - ter get out__ of there fast! She's just a dev - il wo - man

with ev - il on her mind.__ Be - ware the dev - il wo - man, she's gon - na get you!

repeat and fade

DREAMIN'

Words and Music by
ALAN TARNEY and LEO SAYER

FROM A DISTANCE

Words and Music by
JULIE GOLD

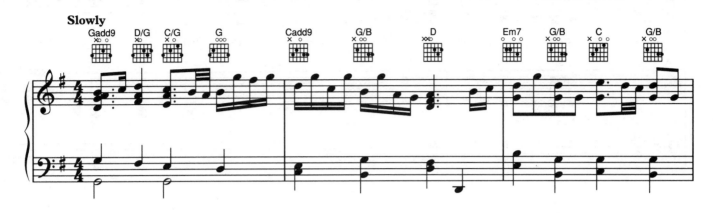

From a dis-tance, the world looks blue___ and green,___ and the
(see additional lyrics)

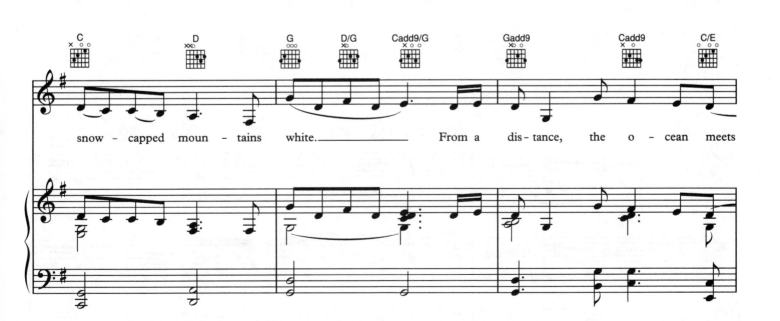

snow - capped moun - tains white.___ From a dis - tance, the o - cean meets

man. God is watch-ing us.___ God is watch-ing us.___ God is

watch-ing us from a dis-tance.

D.%al Coda

From a

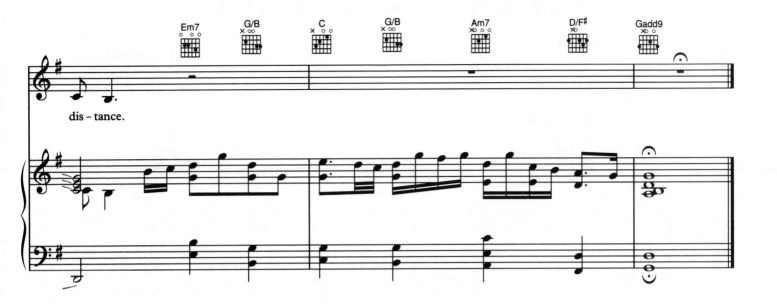

dis – tance.

Verse 2:
From a distance, we all have enough
And no one is in need
There are no guns, no bombs, no diseases
No hungry mouths to feed
From a distance, we are instruments
Marching in a common band
Playing songs of hope, playing songs of peace
They're the songs of every man

Verse 3:
From a distance, you look like my friend
Even though we are at war
From a distance I just cannot comprehend
What all this fighting is for
From a distance there is harmony
And it echoes through the land
It's the hope of hopes, it's the love of loves
It's the heart of every man

IT'S ALL IN THE GAME

Words and Music by
CHARLES DAWES
and CARL SIGMAN

LIVING DOLL

Words and Music by
LIONEL BART

Rock tempo

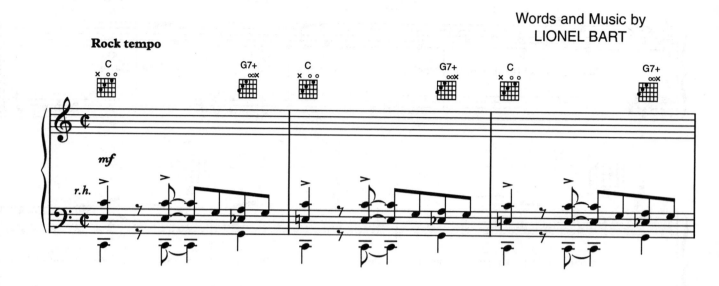

Got my-self a cry - ing, talk - ing, sleep - ing, walk - ing, liv - ing doll, _____

got __ to do my best to please her, just 'cos she's a

Take a look at her hair, it's real! And if you don't be-

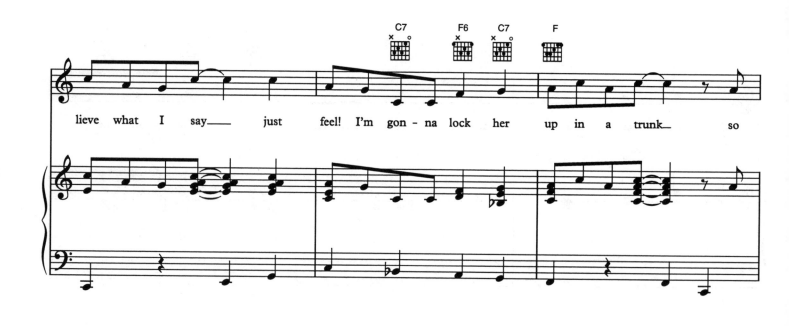

lieve what I say___ just feel! I'm gon-na lock her up in a trunk___ so

D. %. al fine

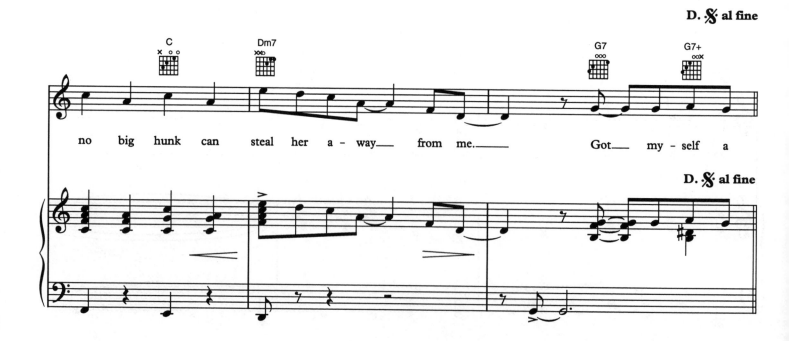

no big hunk can steal her a-way___ from me.___ Got___ my-self a

MILLENNIUM PRAYER

Words and Music by
PAUL FIELD and STEPHEN DEAL

THE MINUTE YOU'RE GONE

Words and Music by
JIMMY GATELEY

oh, so blue, If I could-n't be with you. The min-ute you're gone, I pray,

the min-ute you're gone I say, please don't stay a-way too long

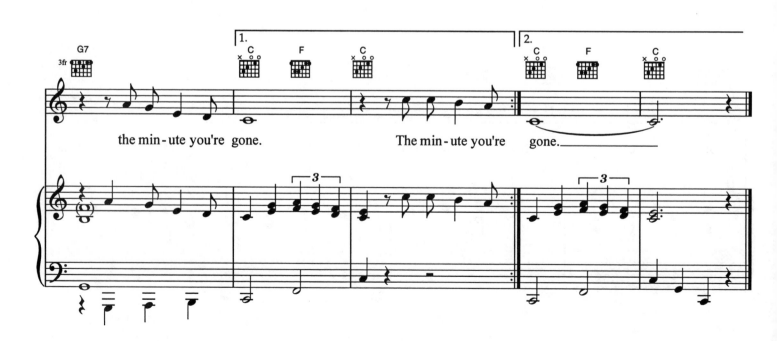

the min-ute you're gone. The min-ute you're gone.

MISTLETOE AND WINE

Words and Music by
KEITH STRACHAN, JEREMY PAUL
and LESLIE STEWART

Easy relaxed tempo

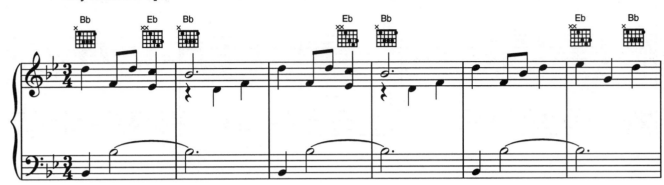

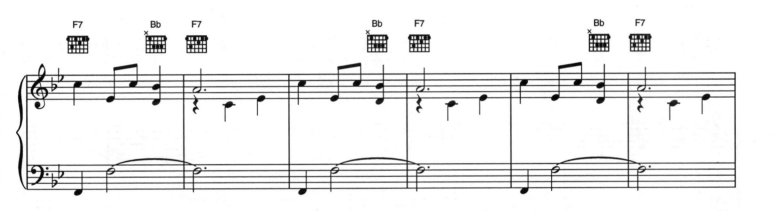

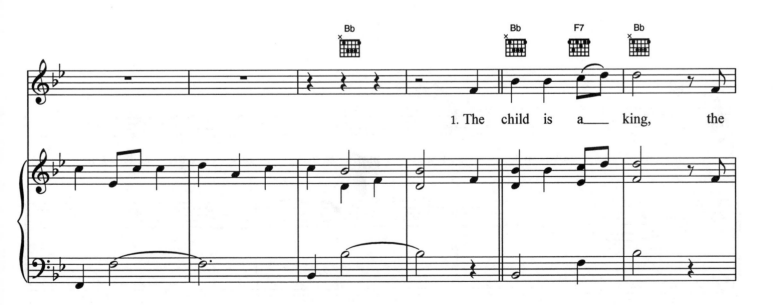

1. The child is a_ king, the

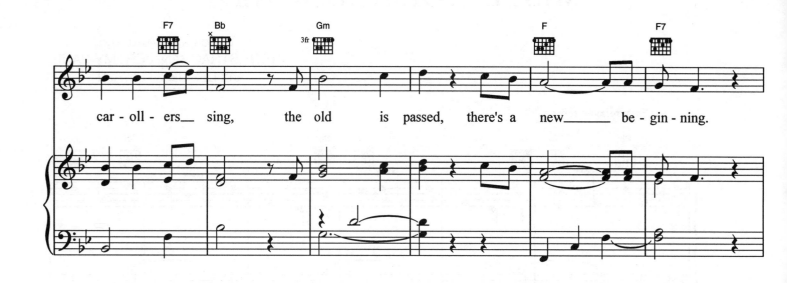

car - oll - ers__ sing, the old is passed, there's a new_____ be - gin - ning.

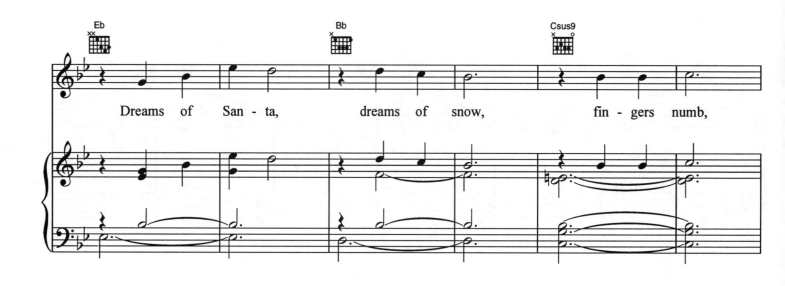

Dreams of San - ta, dreams of snow, fin - gers numb,

fac - es a - glow. It's Christ - mas time, mis - tle - toe and wine,

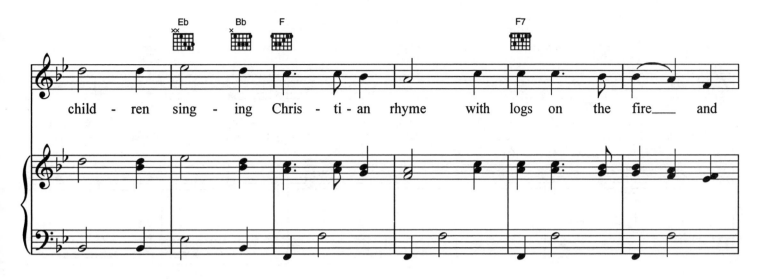

child - ren sing - ing Chris - ti - an rhyme with logs on the fire___ and

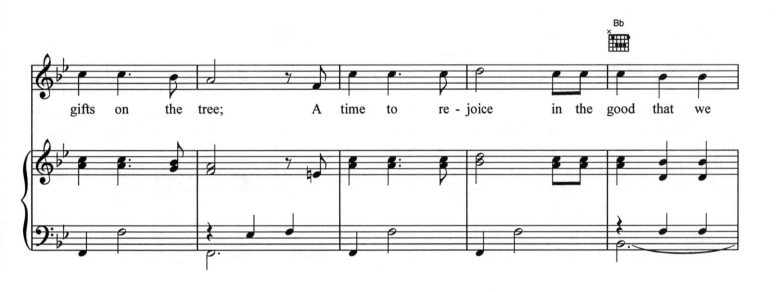

gifts on the tree; A time to re - joice in the good that we

see. 2. A time___ for liv - ing, a time for be - liev - ing, a

3. It's a time___ for giv - ing, a time for get - ting, a

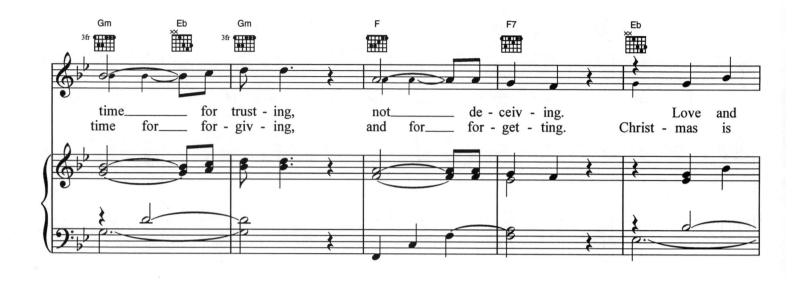

time_____ for trust - ing,   not_____ de - ceiv - ing.   Love and
time for__ for - giv - ing,   and for__ for - get - ting.   Christ - mas is

laugh - ter and joy   ev - er af - ter   Ours for the tak - ing   just
love,_____ Christ - mas is peace;   A time__ for hat - ing__ and

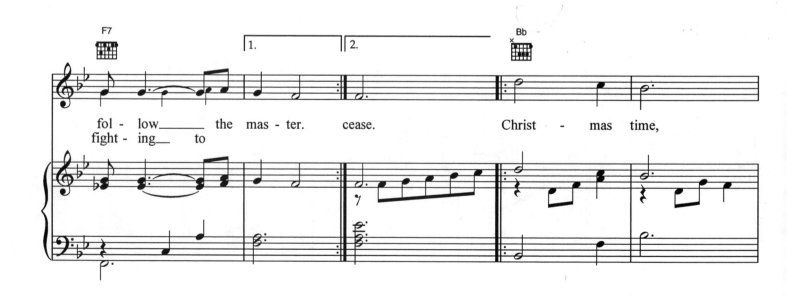

fol - low_____ the mas - ter.   cease.   Christ - mas time,
fight - ing__ to

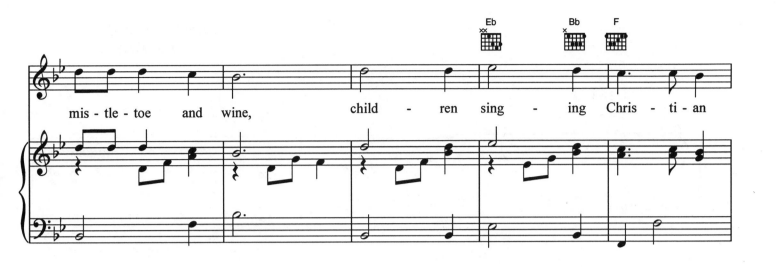

mis - tle - toe and wine, child - ren sing - ing Chris - ti - an

rhyme with logs on the fire___ and gifts on the tree; A

time to re - joice in the good that we see. see.

MOVE IT

Words and Music by
IAN SAMWELL

The rhy-thm that gets— in-to your heart and soul,—

oh, let me tell you ba-by, it's called—

— rock and roll.— They

say it's gon-na die, but hon-ey please let's face— it, oh, well we

move it.

Hey, hey, oh move it.

Uh-huh let's

MY PRETTY ONE

Words and Music by
ALAN TARNEY

1. Well I've dreamed a - bout to - day,___ the same dream in
2. Well I've dreamed a - bout to - day,___ the same dream in so

From a lone - ly prayer,_ I am in_ the_ air._

D.%. al Coda

Coda

No, no - thing

can com - pare with, com - pare with you my pret - ty one._

THE NEXT TIME

Words and Music by
BUDDY KAYE and PHILIP SPRINGER

love_____ with you.

They

2.

you.

When I'm still so ve-ry much in

love_____ with you._____

THE ONLY WAY OUT

Words and Music by
RAY MARTINEZ

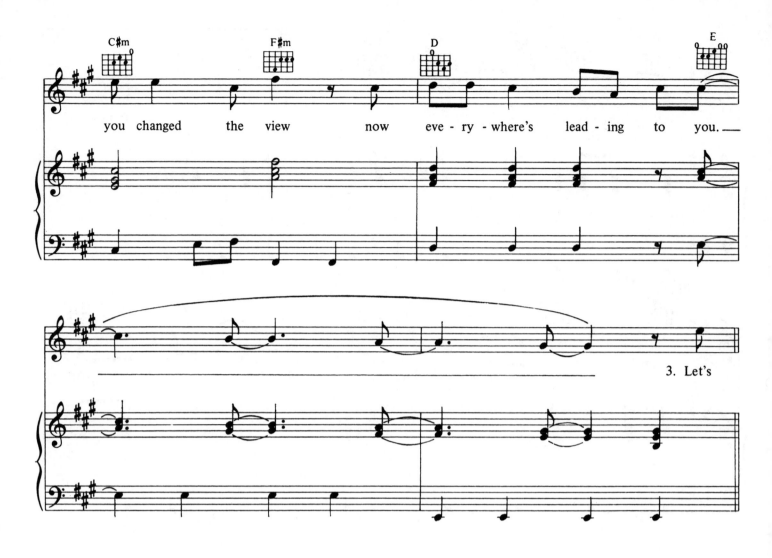

you changed the view now eve - ry - where's lead - ing to you. ___

3. Let's

VERSE 3:   Let's get this thing going let's move it along
Let me do all the things I've been missing so long.
'Cause the only way out is the only way in and it's you.

VERSE: (Instr.)

MIDDLE: I spent a lot of time at the crossroads
Getting that lonely feeling inside
Suddenly you made the rescue you pulled me through
Now let me do something for you.

(Link chords: E/F♯)

[KEY: B]

VERSE 4:   Let's get this thing going let's move it along
Let's do all the things I've been missing so long.
And the only way out is the only way in and it's you,
Yeah the only way out is the only way in and it's you,
Yeah the only way out is the only way in and it's you.

INTRO: (Repeat) +   The only way out
It's the only way in
It's the only way out
It's the only way in . . . . .

(FADE)

PEACE IN OUR TIME

Words and Music by
PETE SINFIELD and ANDY HILL

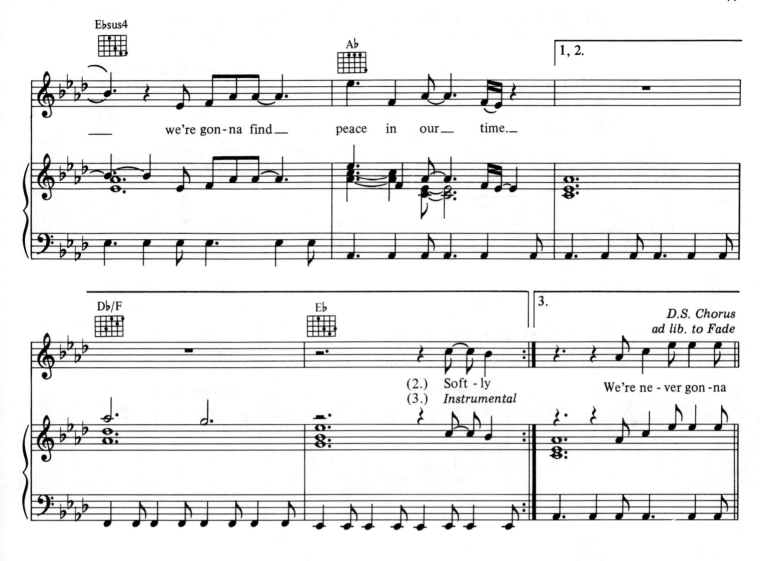

VERSE 2:

Softly softly,
When there is lightning in the sky;
When the rivers are rising
And trouble rolls in on the tide.
We'll keep on keeping on
Till all the tears are dry;
We'll weather the storm and welcome the dawn
Of tomorrow, you and I.
We've gotta have faith and get it fast;
Faith and hope, make it last;
Give us strength to reach the stars;
Put a song in our hearts.

VERSE 3:

INSTRUMENTAL — 12 BARS

We're raising the dust, it's heaven or bust
And we'll see this dream come true.
We're gonna have faith *(faith)*, the road will be long;
But there's hope *(hope)* to carry on;
We'll have strength *(strength)*; we'll never go wrong
With this song in our hearts.

PLEASE DON'T FALL IN LOVE

Words and Music by
MIKE BATT

PLEASE DON'T TEASE

Words and Music by
BRUCE WELCH and PETE CHESTER

You tell me that you love me ba - by, then you say you don't,_

you tell me that you'll come on o - ver, then you say you

won't._____ You love me like a hur-ri cane,_ and then you start to

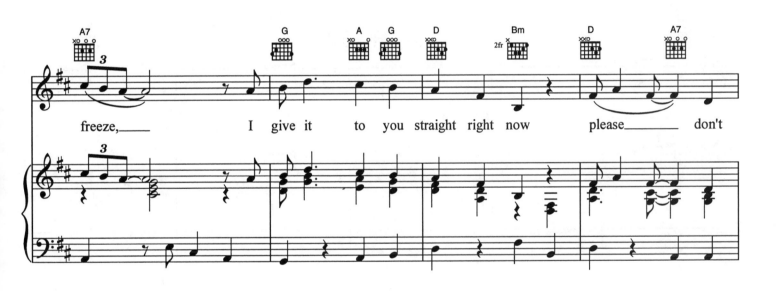

freeze,_____ I give it to you straight right now please_____ don't

tease, you come right out and tell_ me,_ you're out with some - one

tease, oh please don't tease_ me._____ You know it hurts so

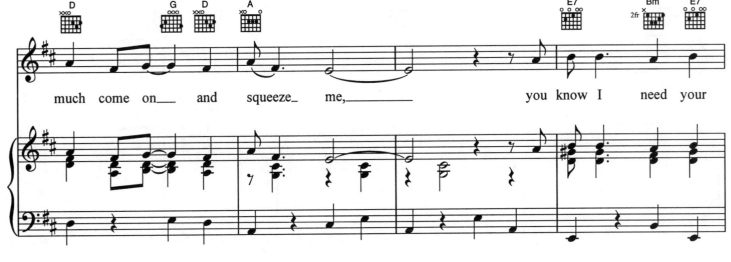

much come on__ and squeeze_ me,_____ you know I need your

ten - der touch, but you tell me that you love me ba - by, then you say you don't,_

88

SHE'S SO BEAUTIFUL

Words and Music by
HANS POULSEN

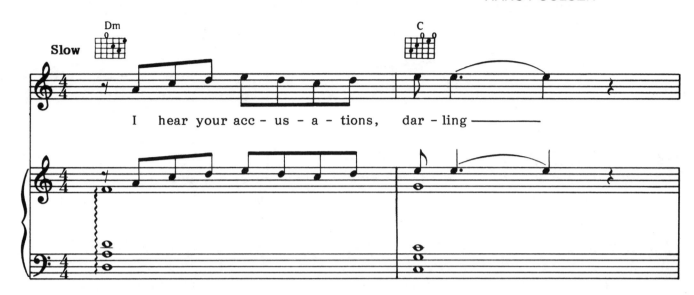

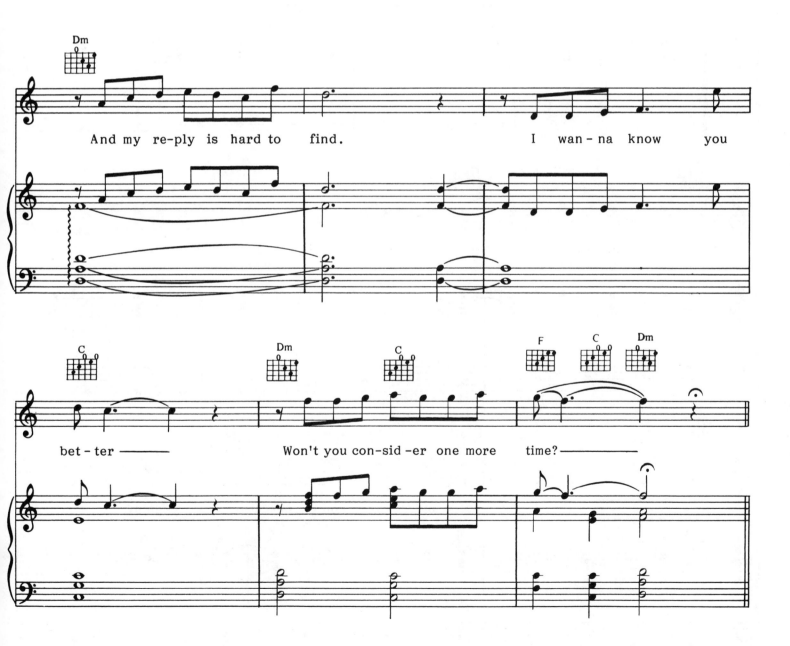

Moderate beat

Riv-er flow to shin—ing sea,— Mount-ain bit—ter blue;—
Ti-ny plan-et spins—through space,— Gives my life— to me,—

Child-ren flow like wa——ter falls,— Sweet our love— re-new.—
Fif-teen bill-ion hu——man beings— Where's our des — tin - y?—

Peace and war and peace— a - gain,—

SOME PEOPLE

Words and Music by
ALAN TARNEY

SUMMER HOLIDAY

Words and Music by
BRUCE WELCH and BRIAN BENNETT

Capo 3

Medium Rock

We're all go-ing on a sum-mer ho-li-day, no more work-ing for a week or two.

Fun and laugh-ter on our sum-mer ho-li-day, no more_ wor-ries for me or you,

TRAVELLIN' LIGHT

Words and Music by
SID TEPPER and ROY C BENNETT

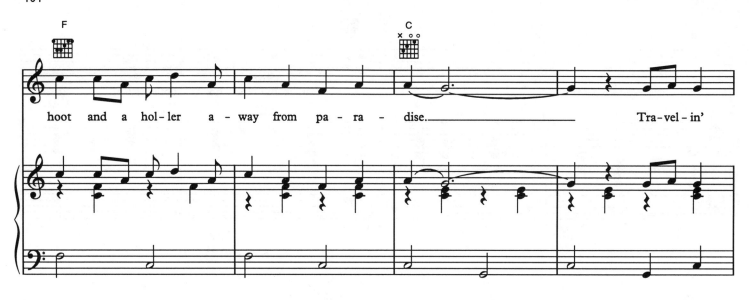

hoot and a hol-ler a-way from pa-ra-dise._____ Tra-vel-in'

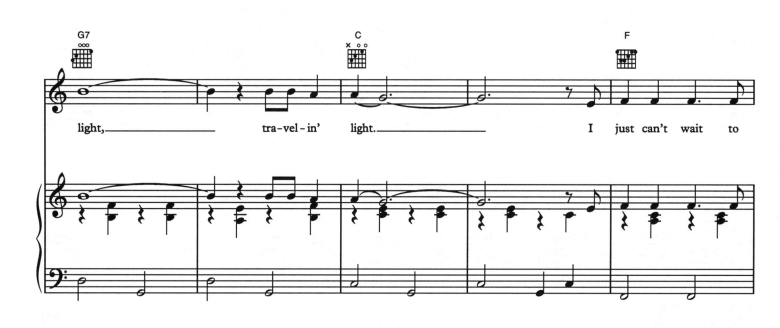

light,_____ tra-vel-in' light._____ I just can't wait to

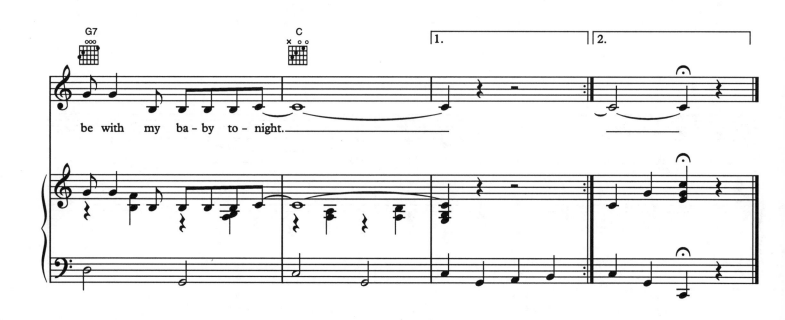

be with my ba-by to-night._____

TRUE LOVE WAYS

Words and Music by
BUDDY HOLLY and NORMAN PETTY

Just you know

why, why you and I will by and

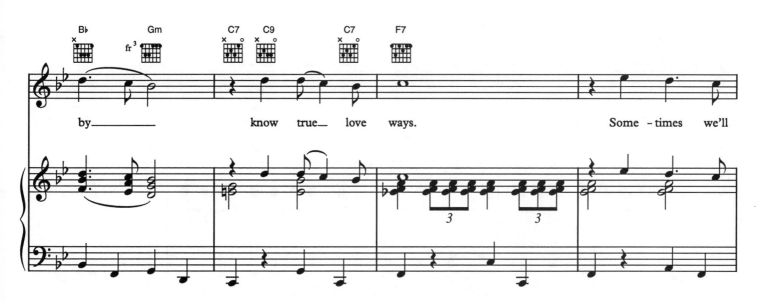

by_____ know true_ love ways. Some-times we'll

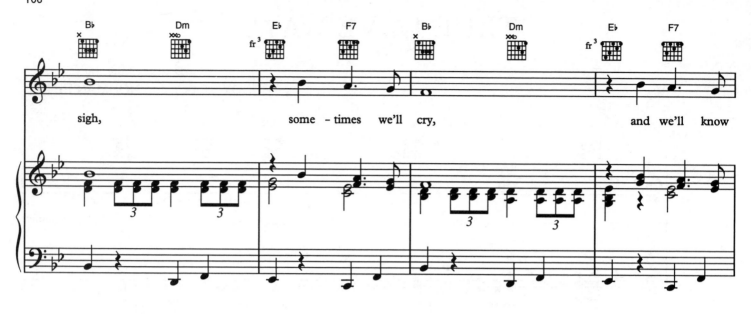

sigh,   some - times we'll cry,   and we'll know

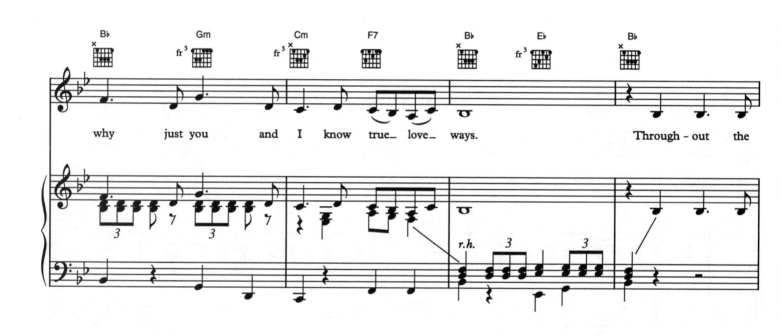

why   just you   and I know true_ love_ ways.   Through - out the

days   our true love ways   will bring us

WE DON'T TALK ANYMORE

Words and Music by
ALAN TARNEY

WIRED FOR SOUND

Words and Music by
B.A. ROBERTSON
and ALAN TARNEY

THE YOUNG ONES

Words and Music by
ROY BENNETT and SID TEPPER

live, love, while the flame‿ is strong, for‿

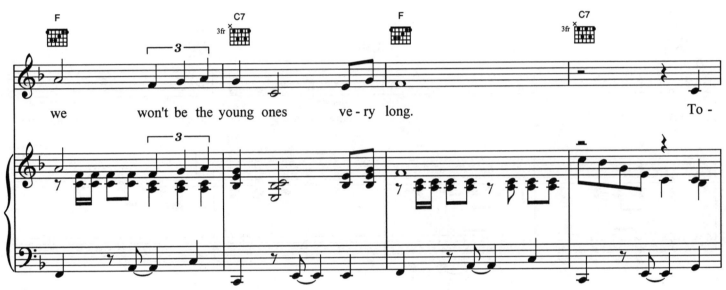

we won't be the young ones ve‿ry long. To‿

mor‿row,‿ why wait 'till to‿mor‿row,‿ to‿

mor - row___ some - times ne - ver comes. So

love, me, there's a song to be sung and the

best time is to sing it while we're young.

Once in ev - 'ry life - time comes a love like this.

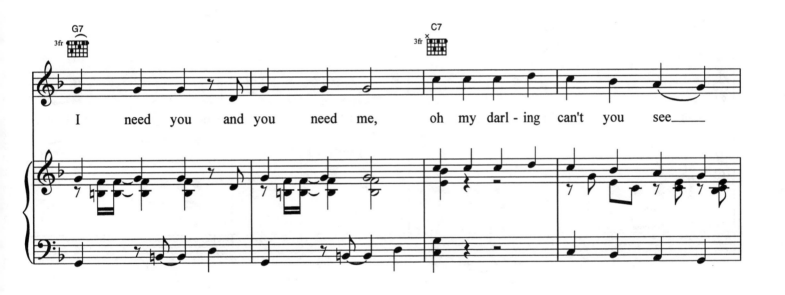

I need you and you need me, oh my darl - ing can't you see____

young__ dreams__ should be dreamed to - geth - er,__

young_ hearts,_ should-n't be a-fraid. And

some day, when the years_ have flown, darl - ing

this we'll teach the young ones of our own. The